Edward
MOLLENHAUER

(1827 – 1914)

"The Boy Paganini" and "The Infant Paganini"
for Violin and Piano

Violin / Violon / Violine

DOWANI International

Violin

The Boy Paganini

Fantasia for Violin and Piano
G Major / Sol majeur / G-Dur

E. Mollenhauer (1827 – 1914)
Edited by H. Scherz

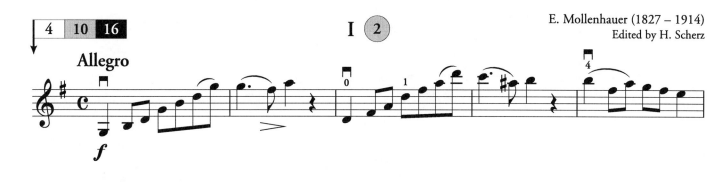

DOW 4523

THEMA

7 13 19

Variation   (+ = pizz. left Hand)

Allegro

The Infant Paganini

Fantasia for Violin and Piano
E Major / Mi majeur / E-Dur

E. Mollenhauer (1827 – 1914)
Edited by H. Scherz

(+ = pizz. left Hand)

DOW 4523

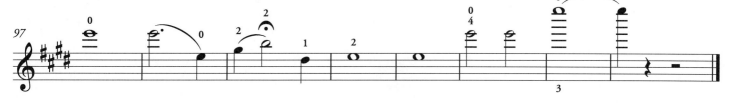

Edward
MOLLENHAUER

(1827 – 1914)

"The Boy Paganini" and "The Infant Paganini"
for Violin and Piano

Edited by
Herbert Scherz

DOWANI International

Preface

With this edition we offer you the two fantasias "The Boy Paganini" and "The Infant Paganini" for violin and piano by Edward Mollenhauer. The German-born violinist, composer and conductor composed operas, symphonies and various pieces for violin. Our edition enables you to work your way through the pieces systematically and in three different tempi with professional accompaniment.

The CD opens with the concert version of each piece (violin and piano). After tuning your instrument (Track 1), the musical work can begin. Your first practice session should be at slow tempo. If your stereo system is equipped with a balance control, you can place either the violin or the piano accompaniment in the foreground by adjusting the control. The violin always remains softly audible in the background as a guide. In the middle position, both instruments can be heard at the same volume. If you do not have a balance control, you can listen to the solo part on one loudspeaker and the piano part on the other. Having mastered the slow tempo, you can now advance to the medium and original tempos. The piano accompaniment can be heard on both channels (without violin) in stereo quality. Each piece has been sensibly divided into subsections for practice purposes. You can select the subsection you want using the track numbers indicated in the solo part. All of the versions were recorded live. The names of the musicians are listed on the last page of this volume; further information can be found in the Internet at www.dowani.com.

The fingering and bowing marks for learners in our volume were provided by Herbert Scherz, a renowned violin teacher who for many years was professor of violin and violin methodology at the conservatories in Lucerne and Zurich. Today, after his retirement, he continues to teach very successfully on a private basis. His pupils have won more than 150 prizes at violin and chamber music competitions; many of them now have successful international careers. In 1985 he founded the "Lucerne Ministrings", an ensemble of children and teenagers up to the age of 16 that has given many concerts in Switzerland and abroad.

We wish you lots of fun playing from our DOWANI 3 *Tempi Play Along* editions and hope that your musicality and diligence will enable you to play the concert version as soon as possible. Our goal is to provide the essential conditions you need for effective practicing through motivation, enjoyment and fun.

Your DOWANI Team

Avant-propos

La présente édition vous propose les deux fantaisies "The Boy Paganini" et "The Infant Paganini" pour violon et piano d'Edward Mollenhauer. Né en Allemagne, ce violoniste, compositeur et chef d'orchestre a écrit des opéras, symphonies et des compositions pour violon. Notre édition vous permet d'étudier les deux morceaux de manière systématique et dans trois tempos différents avec un accompagnement professionnel.

Le CD vous permettra d'entendre d'abord la version de concert de chaque morceau (violon et piano). Après avoir accordé votre instrument (plage n° 1), vous pourrez commencer le travail musical. Votre premier contact avec les morceaux devrait se faire à un tempo lent. Si votre chaîne hi-fi dispose d'un réglage de balance, vous pouvez l'utiliser pour mettre au premier plan soit le violon, soit l'accompagnement de piano. Le violon restera cependant toujours très doucement à l'arrière-plan comme point de repère. En équilibrant la balance, vous entendrez les deux instruments à volume égal. Si vous ne disposez pas de réglage de balance, vous entendrez l'instrument soliste sur un des haut-parleurs et le piano sur l'autre. Après avoir étudié les morceaux à un tempo lent, vous pourrez ensuite travailler à un tempo modéré et au tempo original. Dans ces deux tempos vous entendrez l'accompagnement de piano sur les deux canaux en stéréo (sans la partie soliste). Chaque morceau a été judicieusement divisé en sections pour faciliter le travail. Vous pouvez sélectionner ces sections à l'aide des numéros de plages indiqués dans la partie du soliste. Toutes les versions ont été enregistrées en direct. Vous trouverez les noms des artistes qui ont participé aux enregistrements à la dernière page de la partition ; pour obtenir plus de renseignements, veuillez consulter notre site Internet : www.dowani.com.

Les doigtés et indications des coups d'archet pour élèves proviennent de Herbert Scherz, violoniste et pédagogue de grande renommée. Il fut pendant de nombreuses années professeur de violon et de la méthodique de violon aux Conservatoires Supérieures de Musique à Lucerne et Zurich et donne depuis sa retraite toujours des cours privés avec grand succès. Ses élèves ont reçus plus de 150 prix aux concours de violon et de musique de chambre et beaucoup d'entre eux ont du succès au niveau international. En 1985, il fonda les "Ministrings Luzern", un ensemble d'enfants et de jeunes jusqu'à 16 ans qui donne de nombreux concerts en Suisse et à l'étranger.

Nous vous souhaitons beaucoup de plaisir à faire de la musique avec la collection *DOWANI 3 Tempi Play Along* et nous espérons que votre musicalité et votre application vous amèneront aussi rapidement que possible à la version de concert. Notre but est de vous offrir les bases nécessaires pour un travail efficace par la motivation et le plaisir.

Les Éditions DOWANI

Vorwort

Mit der vorliegenden Ausgabe präsentieren wir Ihnen die beiden Fantasien „The Boy Paganini" und „The Infant Paganini" für Violine und Klavier von Edward Mollenhauer. Der in Deutschland geborene Geiger, Komponist und Dirigent komponierte Opern, Sinfonien und Stücke für Violine. Unsere Ausgabe ermöglicht es Ihnen, die beiden Stücke systematisch und in drei verschiedenen Tempi mit professioneller Begleitung zu erarbeiten.

Auf der CD können Sie zuerst die Konzertversion (Violine und Klavier) eines jeden Stückes anhören. Nach dem Stimmen Ihres Instrumentes (Track 1) kann die musikalische Arbeit beginnen. Ihr erster Übe-Kontakt mit den Stücken sollte im langsamen Tempo stattfinden. Wenn Ihre Stereoanlage über einen Balance-Regler verfügt, können Sie durch Drehen des Reglers entweder die Violine oder die Klavierbegleitung stufenlos in den Vordergrund blenden. Die Violine bleibt jedoch immer als Orientierungshilfe – wenn auch sehr leise – hörbar. In der Mittelposition erklingen beide Instrumente gleich laut. Falls Sie keinen Balance-Regler haben, hören Sie das Soloinstrument auf dem einen Lautsprecher, das Klavier auf dem anderen. Nachdem Sie die Stücke im langsamen Tempo einstudiert haben, können Sie im mittelschnellen und originalen Tempo musizieren. Die Klavierbegleitung erklingt hierbei auf beiden Kanälen (ohne Violine) in Stereo-Qualität. Jedes Stück wurde in sinnvolle Übe-

abschnitte unterteilt. Diese können Sie mit Hilfe der in der Solostimme angegebenen Track-Nummern auswählen. Alle eingespielten Versionen wurden live aufgenommen. Die Namen der Künstler finden Sie auf der letzten Seite dieser Ausgabe; ausführlichere Informationen können Sie im Internet unter www.dowani.com nachlesen.

Die Fingersätze und Bogenstriche in dieser Ausgabe sind speziell für Schüler geeignet und stammen von dem renommierten Violinpädagogen Herbert Scherz. Er war viele Jahre als Professor für Violine und Violinmethodik an den Musikhochschulen in Luzern und Zürich tätig und unterrichtet seit seiner Pensionierung auch heute noch sehr erfolgreich als Privatlehrer. Seine Schüler haben über 150 Preise bei Violin- und Kammermusikwettbewerben erhalten und viele von ihnen sind inzwischen auf internationaler Ebene sehr erfolgreich. 1985 gründete er die „Ministrings Luzern", ein Ensemble mit Kindern und Jugendlichen bis 16 Jahren, das zahlreiche Konzerte im In- und Ausland gibt.

Wir wünschen Ihnen viel Spaß beim Musizieren mit den *DOWANI 3 Tempi Play Along*-Ausgaben und hoffen, dass Ihre Musikalität und Ihr Fleiß Sie möglichst bald bis zur Konzertversion führen werden. Unser Ziel ist es, Ihnen durch Motivation, Freude und Spaß die notwendigen Voraussetzungen für effektives Üben zu schaffen.

Ihr DOWANI Team

The Boy Paganini

Fantasia for Violin and Piano

G Major / Sol majeur / G-Dur

E. Mollenhauer (1827 – 1914)

DOW 4523

THEMA

The Infant Paganini

Fantasia for Violin and Piano
E Major / Mi majeur / E-Dur

E. Mollenhauer (1827 – 1914)

DOW 4523

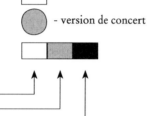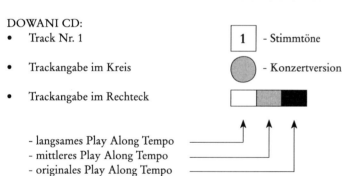